THE TALE OF PETER RABBIT

Adapted from the story and art
by Beatrix Potter
Line art by Lisa Wallace

Copyright © 2014 Dalmatian Press, an imprint of Bendon Publishing International, Inc.
Franklin, Tennessee 37068-2068.
Printed in Ft Wayne, IN, USA.
CE17989/0913 Super Book to Color - THE TALE OF PETER RABBIT / THE TALE OF MRS. TIGGY-WINKLE

Once upon a time there were four little Rabbits, and their names were Flopsy, Mopsy, Cottontail, and Peter.

"My dears," said their mother one morning, "you may go into the fields or down the lane, but don't go into Mr. McGregor's garden."

"Now run along, and don't
get into mischief. I am going out."

Then old Mrs. Rabbit took a basket and her umbrella,
and went through the woods to the baker's.

Dalmatian Press

Flopsy, Mopsy, and Cottontail, who were good little bunnies,
went down the lane to gather blackberries. . .

. . .but Peter, who was very naughty, ran straight away to
Mr. McGregor's garden, and squeezed under the gate!

Dalmatian Press

First he ate some lettuces and some French beans.
And then he ate some radishes.

And then, feeling rather sick, he went to look for some parsley.

Dalmatian Press

But round the end of a cucumber frame,
whom should he meet but Mr. McGregor!

Mr. McGregor jumped up and ran after Peter,
waving a rake and calling out, "Stop, thief."

Dalmatian Press

Peter was dreadfully frightened. He rushed all over the garden,
for he had forgotten the way back to the gate.
He lost both of his shoes!

After losing them, he ran on four legs and went faster,
so that I think he might have got away altogether
if he had not unfortunately run into a gooseberry net.

He got caught by the large buttons on his jacket.
Peter gave himself up for lost, and shed big tears. His sobs were
overheard by some friendly sparrows.

Mr. McGregor came up to catch Peter, but Peter wriggled out
just in time, leaving his jacket behind him.

Peter rushed into the toolshed and jumped into a can—full of water!

Mr. McGregor searched all through the toolshed.
Suddely, Peter sneezed—"Kertyschoo!"

Mr. McGregor was after him in no time!

Peter hopped and hopped until Mr. Mcgregor grew tired of running.
Peter began to wander about, going lippity—lippity—not very fast,
and looking all around.

He found a door in a wall, but it was locked, and there was no room for a fat little rabbit to squeeze underneath.

An old mouse was running in and out over the stone doorstep.
Peter asked her the way to the gate, but she had such a
large pea in her mouth that she could not answer.

Then Peter tried to find his way straight across the garden.
He came to a pond where Mr. McGregor filled his watering cans.
A white cat was staring at some goldfish.
She sat very, very still.

Peter went back toward the toolshed. Suddenly, he heard
the noise of a hoe—scr-r-ritch, scratch, scratch, scritch.
It was Mr. McGregor. And there beyond him was the gate!

Peter started running as fast as he could go toward the gate!
Peter slipped underneath the gate, and was safe
at last in the woods outside the garden.

Mr. McGregor hung up the little jacket and the shoes
as a scarecrow to frighten the blackbirds.

Peter never stopped running till he got home to the big fir tree.
He was so tired that he flopped down upon the nice soft sand on the floor
of the rabbit hole and shut his eyes.

His mother was busy cooking.
She wondered what he had done with his clothes.

I am sorry to say that Peter was not very well during the evening.

His mother put him to bed,
and made some cammomile tea; and she gave a dose of it to Peter:
"One tablespoonful to be taken at bedtime."

But Flopsy, Mopsy, and Cottontail
had bread and milk and blackberries for supper.

THE END

FROM THE WORLD OF
BEATRIX POTTER

JEREMY FISHER

Tom Kitten

Mrs. Tabitha Twitchit

THE TALE OF
MRS. TIGGY~WINKLE

Adapted from the story and art
by Beatrix Potter
Line art by Lisa Wallace

Dalmatian Press

Once there was a little girl called Lucie who was always
losing her pocket-handkerchiefs and pretty, white pinafore.
Tabby Kitten had not seen them.

"Sally Henny-Penny, have you found three pocket-handkins?" Lucie asked.

She asked a little robin, and the robin led her to a hill.
Looking far off, Lucie saw some white things spread upon the grass.

Lucie scrambled up the hill and ran along a steep pathway.

She came to a spring bubbling up from the hillside.
In the sandy path were footprints of a very small person.

At the end of the path she saw some clothes and clothespins—and a door!
Inside, someone was singing.

Lucie knocked. When a voice said, "Who's there?",
Lucie opened the door and found a nice, clean kitchen.

At the table stood a short, round person with an iron in her hand.
She stared at Lucie.

She wore a large apron and her little black nose went sniffle, sniffle, snuffle.
She has twinkly eyes, and under her cap were prickles!

"Who are you?" asked Lucie. "Have you seen my handkins?"
"I'm Mrs. Tiggy-Winkle," she said. "I clean and starch clothes."

"Is that one of my pocket-handkins?" asked Lucie.
"Oh, no," said Mrs. Tiggy-Winkle. "It's Mr. Robin's scarlet coat."

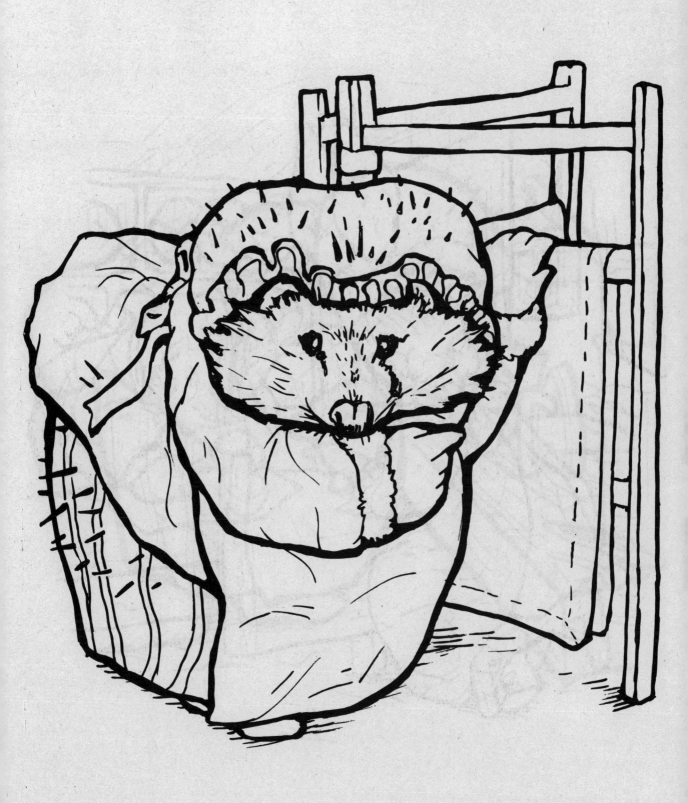

"Is that my pinny?" asked Lucie, seeing something on the clothes rack.
"Oh, no," said Mrs. Tiggy-Winkle. "That's Jenny Wren's tablecloth."

As Mrs. Tiggy-Winkle fetched another hot iron from the fire, Lucie said,
"Oh! I do see my pinny! Right here!"

Mrs. Tiggy-Winkle ironed the pinafore and fluffed the frilly lace.
"How lovely!" said Lucie.

"What are those long yellow things that look like gloves?" asked Lucie.
"These are Sally Henny-Penny's stockings," said Mrs. Tiggy-Winkle.

"And this red handkersniff belongs to old Mrs. Rabbit," said Mrs. Tiggy-Winkle.
"Oh, it *did* so smell like onions!"

"Here's a pair of Tabby Kitten's mittens," said Mrs. Tiggy-Winkle.
"I only have to iron them. She washes them herself."

"My pocket-handkins!" said Lucie happily,
as Mrs. Tiggy-Winkle cleaned three white hankies.

"Now I must air some clothes," said Mrs. Tiggy-Winkle.
"These are the wooly coats of the sweet little lambs."

She hung up small brown mouse coats, a red tailcoat (with no tail!)
of Squirrel Nutkin's, and a very shrunk blue jacket of Peter Rabbit's.

Then Mrs. Tiggy-Winkle made tea—a cup for herself and a cup for Lucie. "My, but she has many prickly hairpins," thought Lucie.

Then they tied up the clothes in bundles.
Mrs. Tiggy-Winkle hid her door key before setting out.

All down the path, Mrs. Tiggy-Winkle delivered the laundry.
Peter Rabbit and Benjamin Bunny popped up from the ferns to meet them.

All the animals and birds said "thank you" to
Mrs. Tiggy-Winkle for their nice clean clothes.

At the bottom of the hill, there was nothing
left to carry except Lucie's own little bundle.

Lucie turned to say "goodnight" to thank the washer-woman,
but Mrs. Tiggy-Winkle was running up the hill—
without her cap and clothes!

And how small she had grown—and how brown and prickly!
Why, Mrs. Tiggy-Winkle was a hedgehog!

Now, some say Lucie had simply dreamed all this.
But *I* know Mrs. Tiggy-Winkle well, so I know it's all true!
—*Beatrix Potter*

THE END